| UK

First published 2018
001

Additional text by Will Mabbitt
Text copyright © The Roald Dahl Story Company Ltd, 2018
Illustrations copyright © Quentin Blake, 2018
Design by Emma Wells at nicandlou.com

The moral right of the author and illustrator has been asserted

Printed in China

A CIP catalogue record for this book is available from the British Library

ISBN: 978–0–241–33082–1

All correspondence to:
Puffin Books, Penguin Random House Children's
80 Strand, London WC2R 0RL

How not to be a TWIT and other WISDOM from ROALD DAHL

Illustrated by Quentin Blake

PUFFIN

INTRODUCTION

Do you suffer from ugly thoughts? Do you struggle with personal hygiene issues? Do you have an ever-growing dislike of children? If you answered YES to fewer than three of these questions then you're definitely lying. After all, it's a well-known fact that the more you grow up, the more of a Twit you become. But worry not, for help is at hand. On your behalf, we've sneaked past the snoring Fleshlumpeater and ventured into the dream cave of Mr Roald Dahl's complete works, pulling out our favourite bits and rearranging them into this phizzwizard of a book for your self-improvement. Take care, not all of his words are fudgemallow delightful, peachy and cream. No, we've taken inspiration from George and his marvellous medicine and mixed in some foul bits too. Because some of us (and by "some of us" I mean all of us) take a secret pleasure in the darkest parts of Roald Dahl's stories – from the extreme stretching of Mike Teavee to the perceived shrinking of Mrs Twit, nobody in the world of Roald Dahl is far away from being squished by a giant peach or being hurled into orbit by an angry elephant. So pull up a chair and pour a glass of frobscottle so we can whizzpop a toast to the man whose wisdom will save us from the encroaching Twittishness that comes with age. Ladies, gentlemen, boys, girls and Vermicious Knids, we proudly present the wisdom of Roald Dahl!

GROWING DOWN

Nowadays, most children are disgusting little brats. It's not their fault. They don't spoil themselves, after all. Having said that, parenting isn't everything. In the world of Roald Dahl, even a couple as loathsome as the Wormwoods can have a child as sparky as Matilda, and there's plenty that adults can learn from kids like her: her thirst for knowledge, her belief in justice and, maybe, if you're lucky, the crushing power of telekinesis . . . In fact, learning from Roald Dahl's young heroes isn't such a bad idea. When seeking role models, it's a mistake to only look upwards. Instead, take a leaf from one of Roald Dahl's books and try growing down a little.

A STODGY PARENT IS

no fun at all.

WHAT A CHILD

WANTS & **DESERVES**

IS A PARENT WHO IS

SPARKY

Danny the Champion of the World

NEVER
GROW
UP,
always
DOWN

George's Marvellous Medicine

"Down with children!
do them in! Boil their bones
and fry their skin!
Bish them, squish them,
bash them, mash them!
Brrreak them, shake them
slash them,
smash them!"

The Witches

It's a funny thing about mothers and fathers.
Even when their own child is the most
disgusting little blister you could ever imagine,
they still think that he or she is wonderful.

Matilda

WHAT'S SO

WONDERFUL

ABOUT BEING A LITTLE BOY ANYWAY?

Why IS THAT NECESSARILY
ANY BETTER THAN BEING A

MOUSE?

LITTLE BOYS HAVE TO GO
TO SCHOOL. MICE DON'T.

The Witches

❝

I don't blame him one bit.
If I was unlucky enough to be married
to Mrs Snoddy, I would drink
something a bit stronger than gin."

"What would you drink, Dad?"

"Poison," he said. "She's a
frightful woman.

❞

Danny the Champion of the World

WORDS CAN HURT YOU

They say reading books can transport you to different worlds. That's a wonderful thing, unless that world happens to be Loompaland and you stumble across a den of ravenous Whangdoodles. Likewise, I'd view a weekend break to Giant Country with suspicion. "Breakfast included" doesn't mean what you think it does, and if anything warrants a one-star review on TripAdvisor it's being ground to a paste inside the salivating mouth of the Bloodbottler. In fact, this reading business sounds pretty dangerous, so if I were you I'd stay inside and watch TV instead. Unless some mischievous Oompa-Loompas have ripped it from the wall and installed a bookshelf in its place. In which case, you'll be looking for a book to start your collection. What a coincidence. There's a great one right here, at this exact moment, in your hand.

Meanings is not important," said the
BFG. "I cannot be right all the time.
Quite often I is left instead of right.

The BFG

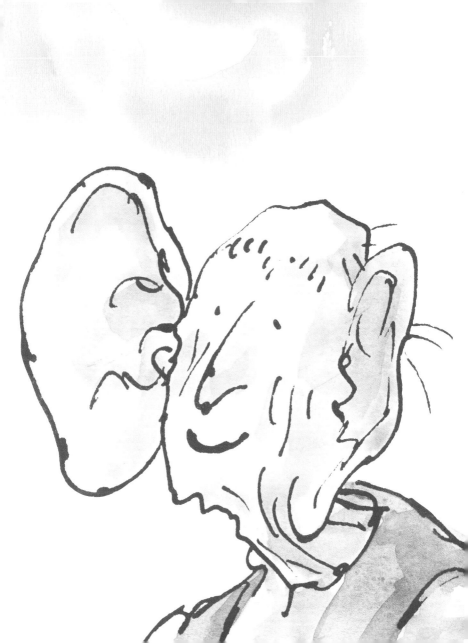

Books

transported her into new worlds and introduced her to amazing people who lived exciting lives. She went on olden-day sailing ships with Joseph Conrad. She went to Africa with Ernest Hemingway and to India with Rudyard Kipling. She travelled all over the world while sitting in her little room in an English village.

Matilda

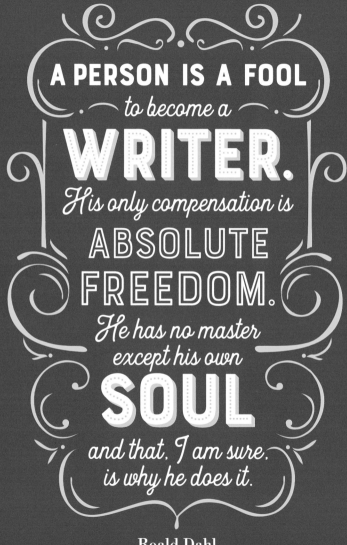

A PERSON IS A FOOL
to become a
WRITER.
His only compensation is
ABSOLUTE
FREEDOM.
He has no master
except his own
SOUL
and that, I am sure,
is why he does it.

Roald Dahl

SO PLEASE,

oh please,

we beg, we pray,

GO THROW YOUR
TV SET AWAY

AND IN ITS PLACE YOU CAN INSTALL A

LOVELY

bookshelf

ON THE WALL

Charlie and the Chocolate Factory

LOOKS IS MORE IMPORTANT THAN BOOKS

We've all changed since we first read a book by Roald Dahl. Probably for the worse. Some of us have become old and bony and shrivelled as prunes, and others . . . well, let's just say that a diet of three boiled chickens smothered with dumplings every day for breakfast, lunch and supper may have taken its toll. No wonder we yearn to recapture our lost youth. But, just like a "new" car from Wormwood's garage, it's a waste of money plastering over the cracks with expensive creams and ointments. Beneath the shiny exterior we'll still be clapped-out old bangers liable to lose bits or spill fluids at the first sign of a steep hill. Refusing to accept we're not the rosy-faced chiddlers we once were is the thinking of a Twit! After all, as Roald Dahl himself writes: "It doesn't matter who you are or what you look like, so long as somebody loves you." And a Twit is hard to love.

If a person has ugly thoughts, it begins to show on the face. And when that person has ugly thoughts every day, every week, every year, the face gets uglier and uglier until it gets so ugly you can hardly bear to look at it.

The Twits

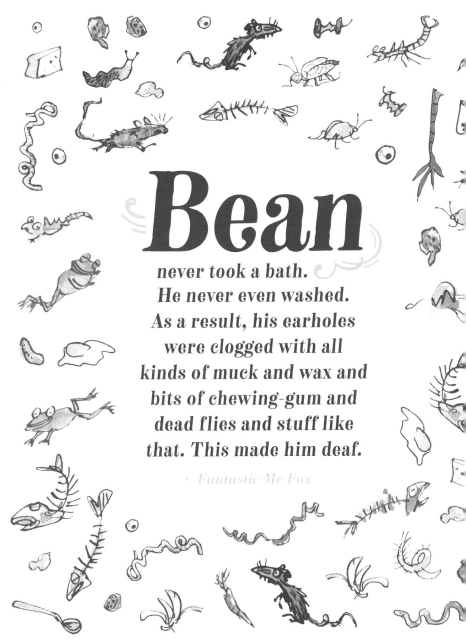

Bean

never took a bath.
He never even washed.
As a result, his earholes
were clogged with all
kinds of muck and wax and
bits of chewing-gum and
dead flies and stuff like
that. This made him deaf.

Fantastic Mr Fox

The

DIRTIER

YOU ARE

THE HARDER IT IS FOR A

WITCH

to Smell

you out

The Witches

· IT'S IMPOSSIBLE ·
TO MAKE YOUR EYES

TWINKLE

if you aren't feeling

twinkly
YOURSELF

Danny the Champion of the World

If you have good thoughts they will **shine** out of your face like **Sunbeams** and you will **ALWAYS LOOK LOVELY**

The Twits

SNOZZCUMBERS ON THE SIDE

Welcome to Roald Dahl's dining table. But be careful not to eat too much. Mr Dahl does not approve of gluttony. Even the most wondrously scrumptious Wonka chocolate, savoured so frugally by young Charlie Bucket, can lead you to be – quite literally – carried away, should you plunge your pudgy face into a whole river of it. Poor Augustus – he was never the same again. A salad then . . . perfect. What's that? You're put off by a mere slug? Just pass it to George's grandma and watch her suck it into her miserable, wrinkled mouth-hole. Give the old lady something to smile about, finally. Still hungry? Some pudding. I'd recommend the doughnuts, stuffed with goose-liver paste by Farmer Bunce's very own grubby fingers. Not for you? Then you can't go wrong with a simple bar of Wonka's Fudgemallow Delight. Next time, perhaps try the moving spaghetti. I wonder what the secret ingredient is?

THE ONE THING

HE LONGED FOR MORE THAN ANYTHING ELSE WAS

Chocolate

Charlie and the Chocolate Factory

"IF I WERE A HEADMASTER I WOULD GET RID OF THE HISTORY TEACHER AND GET A CHOCOLATE TEACHER INSTEAD."

"History of Chocolate",
Roald Dahl's Cookbook

THE SWEET-SHOP OF MY DREAMS
WOULD BE LOADED FROM TOP TO BOTTOM WITH

Caramel Fudge,

SHERBET SUCKERS,

RUSSIAN TOFFEE,

SUGAR SNORTERS

& Butter Gumballs

AND THOUSANDS AND THOUSANDS OF
OTHER GLORIOUS THINGS LIKE THAT.

The Giraffe and the Pelly and Me

"COME AND EAT!"

And they all went over to the tunnel entrance and began scooping out great chunks of juicy golden-coloured peach flesh.

"OH, MARVELLOUS,"

said the Centipede, stuffing it into his mouth.

"DEE-LICIOUS,"

said the Old-Green-Grasshopper.

"JUST FABULOUS,"

said the Glow-Worm.

James and the Giant Peach

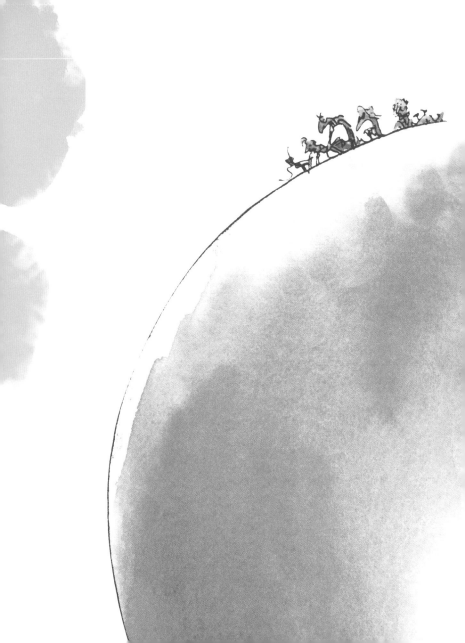

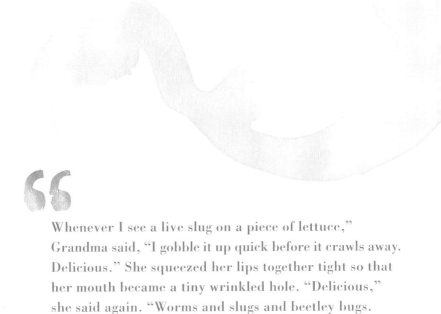

"Whenever I see a live slug on a piece of lettuce,"
Grandma said, "I gobble it up quick before it crawls away.
Delicious." She squeezed her lips together tight so that
her mouth became a tiny wrinkled hole. "Delicious,"
she said again. "Worms and slugs and beetley bugs.
You don't know what's good for you.

George's Marvellous Medicine

ACHIEVING YOUR PHIZZWIZARDS

Dream Country – where dreams begin . . . Some are terrifying trogglehumpers but most are wonderful things full of mystery and magic – and they don't just happen when you're asleep. I'm talking about ambitions. Whether it's achieving true love, fighting for justice, or simply breaking into the queen's bedroom, there's a way to make these dreams come true . . . Go for it! In Roald Dahl's world, spunkiness, pluckiness and initiative are rewarded. As he would say: Go the Whole Hog. It also helps if you have a Big Friendly Giant or some overgrown insects to help you. Maybe that's where I'm going wrong.

A LIFE

IS MADE UP OF A

great

NUMBER

OF SMALL INCIDENTS
AND A SMALL *number*
OF *great* ONES

Going Solo

A little *
nonsense
NOW & THEN
is
RELISHED
by the
wisest
MEN

Charlie and the Great Glass Elevator

NEVER

DO ANYTHING BY HALVES

if you want to get away with it.

BE OUTRAGEOUS.

GO THE WHOLE HOG.

Make sure everything you do is so

COMPLETELY

CRAZY

it's **UNBELIEVABLE.**

Matilda

Dreams
IS FULL OF
MYSTERY
AND *magic.*

DO NOT TRY TO UNDERSTAND THEM.

The BFG

The BFG

And above all, watch with glittering eyes the whole
world around you because the greatest secrets are
always hidden in the most unlikely places.
Those who don't believe in magic will never find it.

Billy and the Minpins